Enjoy!

Andrew
TOFFOLI

hi·stories®
SUSAN BEAR ANTHONY

Based on the life of the women's rights activist, Susan B. Anthony

Written and Illustrated by:
ANDREW TOFFOLI

SUSAN BEAR ANTHONY

Printed in China

ISBN 978-0-9960186-2-3

Library of Congress Control Number: 2018902664

**Our mission is to educate children about history
while using humor and imagination to teach valuable life lessons.**

Please visit us online at: **www.littlegerm.com**

10 9 8 7 6 5 4 3 2 1

For Cooper

Susan Bear Anthony, an outspoken and determined bear, was born in Adams, Massachusetts in 1820.

As a cub,
Susan was taught by her father to
to stick up for herself.

Her father always stated,
"To be great,
you cannot hibernate!"

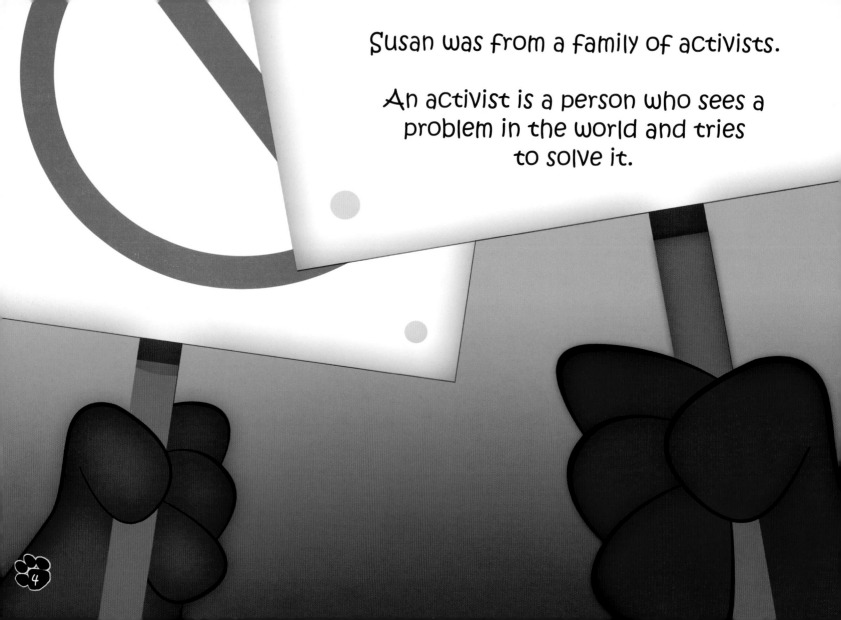

Susan was from a family of activists.

An activist is a person who sees a problem in the world and tries to solve it.

Susan worked hard in school
and became a teacher.

It was one of the few jobs
a woman could have.

She worked her paws to the bone, but she quickly noticed that males were paid more.

She remarked,
"I do the same work as him,
so why is my wallet so thin?"

7

In fact, at this time, women were not allowed to vote, buy property, or have freedom of speech.

Susan was furious!

Enough was enough!

So she packed her bags...

...and set out to debate all across the United States.

During her travels,
she would meet other women
who would join her cause.

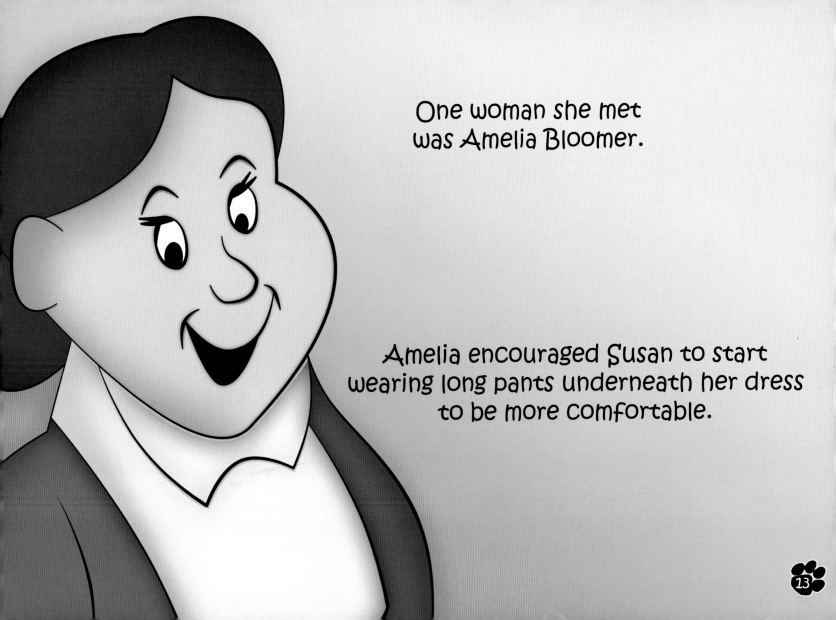

One woman she met
was Amelia Bloomer.

Amelia encouraged Susan to start
wearing long pants underneath her dress
to be more comfortable.

Amelia stated,
"A heavy dress is irritating and hot,
but with bloomers it is not!"

Later she would meet
Elizabeth Cady Stanton,
one of the strongest leaders for
women's rights.

Elizabeth would always say,
"All women need to *stand together*
for the same rights,
even if it takes all day and night!"

16

To spread the word, Susan and Elizabeth published a newspaper called, *The Revolution.*

The articles talked about the problems workers faced and their solutions.

The Revolution

Election day arrived...

...Susan was going to vote !

In the election of 1872, Susan went to cast her vote with zest...

...but in turn,
was placed under arrest!

Susan persisted and would speak in Congress...

24

year after year...

...after year

...after year.

27

Finally in 1920, the 19th Amendment
to the Constitution passed
giving all women the right to vote.

Susan's hard work was rewarded.

In 1979, the United States Treasury Department honored Susan Bear Anthony by putting her portrait on the dollar coin.

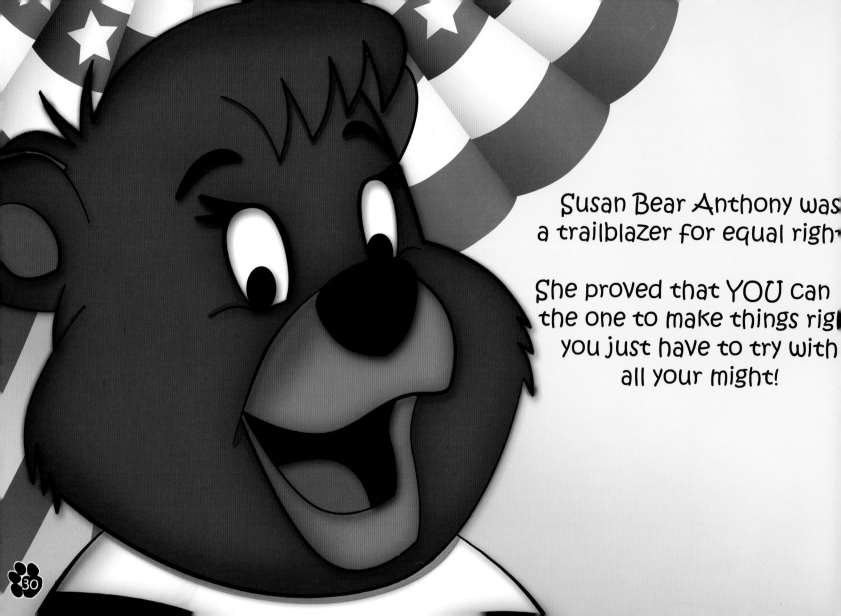

Susan Bear Anthony was
a trailblazer for equal righ

She proved that YOU can
the one to make things rig
you just have to try with
all your might!

Words to know:

Activist: Noun - a person who campaigns for some kind of social change.

Debate: Noun - a discussion between two people or groups who disagree on an important subject.

Hibernate: Verb - to be in an inactive or dormant state; sleep during winter.

Outspoken: Adjective- a person who has lots to say about a particular subject.

Trailblazer: Noun - a person who is the first to do something that other people do later.

Zest: Noun - enthusiastic enjoyment.

George
Washington
Carfur™

Coming Soon
from
hi·stories®

Marco Hippolo™

Ludpig Van
Beethoven™

Abrahound
Lincoln™

Juan Ponce De LeBison™   Bark Twain™   Sir Ibis Newton™   Namolean Bonaparte™

JoHorn Gutenberg™